DICK BARTON

SPECIAL

ANNUAL

D1438655

Published by

Rainbow Books

BROWN WATSON

A Howard & Wyndham Company.
135 WARDOUR ST. LONDON W.1. ENGLAND.

Printed in Holland.

©1978 DEMOB Limited
Pages 7-12; 52-53 60. Photograph ©BBC.

DICK BARTON

–Genesis of a Hero

There is something wholly unique about Dick Barton. . . . Parents hardly ever leave the room, snorting disgust when the show comes on. They make none of the usual remarks about 'just kids' stuff' and disappear into kitchen, study, allotment or squash courts. They sit down and stay. Ever wondered about that? Why it is that Mum and Dad, and more than a few grandparents, seem to visibly care about Dick Barton, Snowy White and Jock Anderson more than any other television heroes?

The answer is nostalgia.

More so than Cmdr. James Bond, more even than Batman and Robin, *Dragnet*'s Sgt. Joe Friday or *Star Trek*'s Capt. Kirk—

Capt. Dick Barton was most parents' first hero. From way back in the dark and drab years just after the end of the second world war, when television for many still sounded like something in science-fiction and radio was king. When Barton and his indefatigable cohorts were the modern musketeers of radio's first all-action serial—a sort of prototype 007, though imbued with far more courtesy, civility and chivalry, and the vital cliff-hanging touch of *The Perils of Pauline.*

Between 1947 and 1951, every night of the working week, Monday to Friday, for nearly four years, younger Britain came to a standstill at 6.45 pm, switching the radio

over to what was then known as The Light Programme (today's Radio 2) and waiting, full of hushed expectancy on the literal edge of their seats.

'**The time is quarter to seven. This is the BBC Light Programme,**' said the duty continuity-announcer, with all the Beeb's traditional tones of national importance. His voice was immediately followed by the most exciting signature-tune ever devised by man—it's still with us today in the television version; and it's still the best opener around — 'The Devil's Gallop' by Charles Williams. *Dum-de-dum Dah!* *Dum-de-dum.* . . . Just a few bars of that and you were hooked. For life.

Far right, top: the three main characters, Dick Barton, Snowy White and Jock Anderson during a broadcast. Bottom right: actors sorting out some script problems before going on air. Right: Noel Johnson as Dick Barton.

Above: a dramatic scene from a Dick Barton episode. Right: Snowy White, left (played by John Mann) and Jock Anderson (Alex McCrindle).

Then, the announcer would invoke like some magic spell of yore, four more essential words, and the entire country would be in thrall. *'Dick Barton—Special Agent!'*

For the next fifteen rushalong minutes, ears were glued to radios which were still known rather portentously as wirelesses. All other activity ceased. Eating was postponed; drinking stopped with cups of tea held, frozen in mid-air en route to gaping mouths; homework or 'prep' was forgotten; football and cricket became secondary; gardening simply lost its allure—and the bath-water of the nation cooled in empty tubs.

Everyone craned forward, so as not to miss one word of the rip-roaring adventures of the straightest, purest, most noble and gentlemanly hero in Britain . . . A Military Cross winner at Dunkirk, former member of a crack commando unit in the Mid-East, S.E. Asia and Europe war zones, and since November 5, 1945, a demobbed army captain, bowler-hatted by Whitehall, foot-loose and restless amid the restraints of a drab post-war existence.

He set up shop as a special agent. An inquiry agent, that is, or private detective really; no secret agent. The life suited him. Danger was his business. He was devoted to righting wrongs, sorting wheat from chaffe, rescuing the goodies and depositing the baddies in clink, in the fastest-moving of any radio serial, before or since, which ended, always ended every night with our hero, or his everloyal chums, deep in some ghastly mire. Up to their singular or collective neck, more often than not, in a locked, windowless basement, filling with torrents of water . . . bound and gagged aboard a plane, from which an evil pilot had just parachuted . . . handcuffed together inside a blazing room . . . shut inside a refrigerator . . . or as happened on one memorable occasion, cast adrift on a synthetic iceberg floating in mid-atlantic.

In short: the end seemed in sight. Yet again. Morecambe and Wise time: Get out of that!

Then, 'The Devil's Gallop' rolled anew and the announcer returned, more rapidly and staccato this time. **'Can Dick Barton destroy the time-bomb? Will Jock and Snowy get the message in time? Why have the gemstones been removed from the safe? Listen again to-morrow night to another installment of . . .** (pause for breath; and goodness but he

Left to right: Jock Anderson (Alex McCrindle), Dick Barton (Noel Johnson), Inspector Burke (Colin Douglas) and Snowy White (John Mann).

Left: Duncan Carse as Dick Barton and right: Duncan Carse and his Finnish wife recording the series 'Anglo Finnish Families'.

needed it) . . . *Dick Barton— Special Agent;'*

Oh, the agony of it. A whole day to wait!

Next came the news and Radio Newsreel. Very dull stuff in comparison to the derring-do exploits which filled the hearts and minds and conversation of the younger British generation for the rest of the twenty-four hours until 'The Devil . . .' galloped again—*Dum-de-dum Dah*; *Dum-de-dum*—and with something closely akin to the inevitable leap and bound, Barton was free. Only to fall into another dastardly trap by 7 pm the following night. 'Great heavens—there's *no* floor in the lift!'

Ah! those were the days and

no mistake. As the rivetting television series is now cleverly reviving for us. If the series is good (which it is) it's because most of the people responsible for it were among those young hordes who never missed their 6.45 pm appointment with thrills and spills. Or if they did, they always caught up with the week-end omnibus edition. Now they're living it all over again, the hard way—finding pictures to match what they saw in their youthful imaginations more than a quarter of a century ago.

In those days, such radio serials were called soap-operas; because in America, the continuing stories helped sell soap, among other commodities via

the commercials. And indeed, Capt. Barton was born to replace the first ever BBC radio serial, *The Robinsons*—a cross between the *Mrs. Dale's Diary* to come and *Crossroads,* with all the drama quotient such a mix implies. Serials, long-running sagas over and beyond any normal six-week adaption of a classic book by Dickens or Hardy, were still a new genre on British radio. But the new Light Programme chieftain, Norman Collins, wanted something more original than just another domestic series wringing tension out of Grandma's operation and cousin Jack's business going pfffht!

Collins had an assistant look into the notion of a 'cloak-and-dagger soap-opera'. Producer Martyn Webster got together with writers Geoffrey Webb and Edward J. Mason (who later created Dick Barton's still-running successor, *The Archers*) and action-packed scripts were soon flowing. With Broadcasting House studios fully occupied, space had to be found at BBC Birmingham to record the first six pilots, or test shows. Actor Noel Johnson (like Barton, a wounded evacuee of Dunkirk) was

A general view of a radio studio during rehearsal.

Above: left to right, Inspector Burke (Colin Douglas), Dick Barton (Duncan Carse) and Snowy White (John Mann). Middle: Our three heroes, Dick Barton, Jock and Snowy. Left: some other actors from an early Dick Barton recording.

selected to play the hero; three days a week were reserved for rehearsing and recording a week's batch of five episodes. The portents looked good—except for the right-sounding heroic name.

At first, the ultra-decent hero was called Bill Barton . . . which just didn't sound right, somehow. Not middle-class enough for the BBC. The full list of probable names from the writers included various sea-worthies: Peter Drake, Rex Drake, Michael Drake. They also suggested Peter Fenton or Peter Grant. Peter, obviously, had a good classy ring about it, but further down at the end of the list came the favourite surname at least: Roger Barton, Rex Barton, Pat Barton, Peter Barton (of course) and Bill Barton. Not a Bob in sight, although that was chosen as his father's name; not a Richard or its diminutive, Dick. That came in the end not from the writers, but, refreshed from a holiday, Norman Collins himself.

Perhaps he had been reading the 1931 book, *Four Frightened People* by Mrs. E. Arnot Robertson. In her novel, she had introduced a character called Dick Barton, the hero of a boys' serial, 'full of sterilised ideas of chivalry, modesty and un-obtrusive courage.' *Very* prophetic.

On September 14, 1946, Norman Collins (an author himself: *London Belongs To Me*) sent a memo to the Head of BBC Drama, Val Gielgud. 'I know that you'll hate hearing this, but the first installment of the *Dick Barton* series . . . is really awfully good . . . just what we want. On this showing, the thing will run for years.'

Gielgud, more used to presenting Shakespeare, Chekhov, Trollope and some more modern playwrights on radio, was far from appalled. 'On the contrary,' he annotated the memo, 'if you're pleased, so am I.' So was the programme director of the Midlands region, Denis Morris, in Birmingham. 'Several of us have pencilled in our diaries, 7 October 1967 for the 21st birthday party.' he said.

And so the show began on Monday, October 7, 1946. Dick Barton, Snowy White and Jean Hunter epically survived the first adventures, solving and saving all. The stalwart Scot, Jock Anderson, joined the troupe by Episode 17.

At first, it's safe to say that only the most ardent fans of *The Robinsons* noticed the new programme. They turned on to their favourite radio show and found the ancient battle of good v. evil going on—and very loudly—instead of cosy domestic bliss. Not a lot of them liked

it. But the word spread soon enough among youngsters, starved of comics among other entertainments in the mid-40s. Here was something much better—an audio-comic strip. Within two weeks the Communist *Daily Worker* newspaper (now *The Morning Star*) denounced the serial as being 'so bad as to be almost beyond criticism'; except their own that was. Capt. Barton, the paper went on to comment was a crypto-fascist. Some Paris film critics have said the same thing about the *Star Wars* heroes. It's a silly comment, but must amuse the original Jock Anderson, actor Alex McCrindle. He happens to be in the *Star Wars* cast, as the rebel forces leader General Dodonna, and thereby still labelled Fascist 32 years later . . . !

The major brouhaha over Dick Barton ignited in that most illustrious of all British newspapers, *The Times*. A letter from a certain Mrs. W. Wright-Newsome fretted about the possible harmful effects of the serial upon children. They were, she alleged, more concerned with what Dick Barton would get up to next, than about their own future or the future of England. This view started an avalanche of pro and anti mail, and Barton's alter-ego, Noël Johnson, joined in the reams of correspondence himself. By January 3, 1947, Barton had become important enough to be the subject of one of those most exalted *Times* editorials.

'*Dick Barton with that manly, ringing voice of his may not be everyone's idea of a perfect hero, but he must be gratified by the number of voices that have been raised on his behalf. . . . Children are generally rather more tough and sensible than those who fear the influence of serial or cinema are apt to believe, and after all Dick manages to squeeze his hair-raising adventures into a quarter of an hour—and a quarter of an hour can be a refreshing break in a "prep" (homework) which can often run to six times that length.'*

The media coverage of the programme never let up, and this remember in the days of no television heroics from Steve Austin, Jack Regan, Theo Kojak or Starsky and Hutch. The headlines flowed, thick (very thick) and fast. Any and everything could be blamed on Dick Barton, much the way delinquency / punk rock / football hooliganism / muggings / race rows/etc are nowadays blamed on television.

DICK BARTON — TOO THRILLING FOR GIRLS? HEADMISTRESS SAYS 'YES'

DICK BARTON DOES NOT HARM CHILDREN— SCHOOL DOCTOR

DICK BARTON—A PARISH DECIDES, SOME SAY IT'S BAD, SOME GOOD

ANOTHER GRAND-MOTHER PRAISES DICK BARTON

SHOULD DICK BARTON DIE?

In the middle of it all, a Labour government minister, Herbert (later Lord) Morrison announced he liked the programme. George Bernard Shaw, perhaps naturally enough, said he didn't. Then again, G.B.S. admitted he never listened to it. He was no doubt more taken with another headline: **AT 16,**

HE PREFERS GBS TO DICK BARTON.

The fact that Barton was blamed for the rise in juvenile crime was, of course, utter rubbish, and neatly put down by one magistrate faced with two children on a house-breaking charge. Their father blamed their exploits on—who else?—poor old Capt. Dick. The judge rebuked him in court: 'Dick Barton doesn't take other people's property.'

Indeed, once the BBC latched on to the surprising fact that children recognised the comic-book elements of the serial (some surprise!) and comprised the majority audience, an immensely strict code of conduct was concocted for their hero to abide by. Barton had to quit smoking, drinking (the villains could imbibe) and very quickly lost his girl-friend, Jean Hunter. His swiftly re-written life - style became closer to Baden - Powell's *Scouting For Boys*—or *Boys' Own Paper* at least—than Mickey Spillane.

He could, for example, employ certain deceits in his assignments—but he could never be heard telling an outright lie. Heaven forbid! He never carried a gun, refrained from all covert, underhand or abusive action — and certainly, never broke the law himself. He was only permitted to punch his way

out of trouble—Rule 5: 'clean socks on the jaw'—and then only if and when heavily outnumbered. He became more chivalrous than the Knights of the Round Table, a shining, whiter than white, biologically pure knight in trilby and belted-raincoat armour. He was, if you like, turned into an utter square. Except the way he used his wits more than mere muscle was far from square. It was simply terrific!

After his programme, there was scant necessity for the announcer to warn youngsters not to copy his flying or under-water - swimming techniques, as with TV's *Batman* and *Man From Atlantis*. In fact, despite all the headline-seeking moans from religious and educational bodies, there was nothing but good to come from imitating Dick Barton. One boy following his hero's traits, helped have a criminal arrested. **DICK BARTON FAN TRAILED CROOK — BOY PRAISED IN COURT** ran that headline.

Another lad, a fifteen-year-old in Cornwall, owed his life to emulating this very special agent. He had fallen on a railway line as a train was heading right towards him—fast! If that sounded a typical Dick Barton 7 pm cliff-hanger, so was the result. The lad

Left: a point of interest noted by Dick Barton (Gordon Davies) centre. Middle: the cast of a Dick Barton episode gather at rehearsals and bottom: Gordon Davies as Dick Barton.

walked away from the perilous incident with nary a scratch. 'I listen to Dick Barton,' he explained to the papers. 'And I did exactly what he did when he got under a train—lay flat and still.' Today, youngsters suck Kojak lollipops and ruin their teeth.

No matter what the newspapers reported, for good or ill, nothing but nothing stopped every youngster's all-important date at 6.45. The success of the serial was its speed, part of a brilliant design by the writing and production team. The big secret, as outlined by writer George Nobbs in his book, *The Wireless Stars,* was giving every episode three major dramatic peaks.

The first was the escape from the previous night's trap— usually resolved inside two minutes, and always eminently plausible with Barton or his associates simply making use of some escape-route the listeners had not cottoned on to the night before. Next, came the story's latest chapter, or plot development — given extra

pace and action by setting most of the dialogue in cars, planes, boats; anything speedy. This action led to the second peak, the entrance of a new theme or character highlighting the all-important five minutes of the third and to - be - continued peak—the cliff-hanger. Friday night's climax had to be a real shaker, making sure everyone tuned in again on Monday night. They always did.

If the serial was meticulously controlled, things got hugely out of hand for the actor who *was* Dick Barton for the whole country. Noël Johnson was spending £1,000 a year of his own earnings on postage to his fans; but he wasn't getting any other kind of acting work. As happened before him to Johnny Weismuller as Tarzan, Buster Crabbe as Flash Gordon, George Reeves as Superman, and more recently Sean Connery and now Roger Moore as 007, the star became over-identified with the one role. To be frank, the role took over the actor's life.

In 1949, Noël Johnson had

had enough; he quit the show. Duncan Carse, something of a real-life Barton adventurer, known for various Antarctic exploration expeditions, took over the part. In between the radio Bartons, Don Stannard played him in three sub-standard Hammer films. The first, not un-naturally was titled *Dick Barton, Special Agent* (1948); followed by *Dick Barton Strikes Back* (1949) and *Dick Barton At Bay* (1950). All three were nothing much to leave home for; more 'quickies' than speedy, they lacked the radio's sheer zest, and turned plausible comic - strip into adolescent strip-cartoon.

By 1951, although the zipa-long sparkle was still evident on radio, Dick Barton had lost most of his audience. The original fans had matured into other spheres, and the fresh generation of children and potential radio-fans were mesmerised by the TV set in the corner. Dick Barton faced his final cliff-hanger. This time he could not avoid the swingeing axe above his cool head. He was pushed right into a corner and soundly thrashed . . . by Dan and Doris Archer.

Now he's back in action, continuing from exactly where he was cut off in his prime 27 years ago, righting wrongs and putting villains inside; and on the very medium which was supposed to have proved his ultimate nemesis. Television. He's as good, as noble as ever; straighter than any arrow. And introduced as only he can be, by that thumping, thundering, thrilling testament to his tenacity . . . *Dum-de-dum Dah*; *Dum-de-dum.* Long may he gallop.

Left: Gordon Davies as Dick Barton looking ever inch a superhero and bottom: actors during a broadcast.

TONY VOGEL
– the Special Agent who wants to be a farmer

Every week he's the steely-eyed, iron-willed hero putting paid to the careers of some of the meanest villains ever created for television. They drop him into the most fiendish traps imaginable. But Barton lives on his courageous wits and manages to slip the net every time and turn the tables on the arch-criminals and put them firmly behind bars . . . before throwing away the key.

He's the best all-British hero. Better than James Bond, because he doesn't have a brief-case full of impossible gadgets. Better than Hazell, because you can actually understand what he says.

And yet the excellent actor who brings Barton to such vivid — memorable — life maintains that he is in the wrong profession.

Tony Vogel has acted in just about every-thing—from Shakespeare's Caliban in *The Tempest* to the apostle Andrew in Franco Zefferelli's moving, masterly and mammoth tv-film of *Jesus of Nazareth*. Tony's credits, on stage, screen and television are the envy of any actor. But he has a secret yearning to take up the very kind of life which replaced the derring-do Dick Barton way of life on radio all these years ago—farming.

'I'd really like to have been a farmer,' he declares, and very passionately. 'I still hope I might manage it some day.'

These agricultural ambitions, on the face of it an odd choice for such an adventurous hero, are inspired by his immensely happy childhood. Tony Vogel was born near Oxford in 1942, but he was brought up on a smallholding in

Cornwall.

And he's never forgotten it. . . .

'The best life any kid could have. We had goats and chickens and lots of other animals. And we were self sufficient long before it became fashionable in *The Good Life*.'

Trouble was, like all good things in life, even more so in a child's life, it didn't last. 'When I was ten we moved to London and I cried myself to sleep every night. I hated it in London. Still do !'

On the other hand, his four children adore life in the metropolis. Eleven-year-old Anna, Toby aged nine and Daniel aged four, live in London with their mother; Tony's first wife. Tony's other child is Felix, just three years old. 'I'd love them to experience the sort of youth I had in Cornwall. But they'd hate leaving London, as much as I hated leaving the country.'

After completing his education at Westminster School, Tony Vogel spent a year back in the fresh-air life—on building sites, not farms— before deciding to enter R.A.D.A., the Royal Academy of Dramatic Art—birthplace of so many fine British acting talents. Since then, of course, the acting life has taken him all over Britain. And beyond.

While he enjoyed many of the plays—and some of his films—he was never overly keen on the environments he worked in. Whenever he could, he'd quickly slip out of the big cities and major towns and quite frankly, run away from people. All people. 'I'm not a very sociable animal,' he confesses.

For instance, he spent one long period living in a lonely farm-house in Derbyshire. Then, after two full years of Shakespeare, Chekhov, Kopit, Nichols, and Stoppard with the Tyneside Theatre Company at Newcastle University Theatre, he took to the wilds again and simply disappeared from view.

'I found a little house in Northumberland—a good mile or so away from anything like a road.

No water. No electricity. And everything else had to be fetched and carried back to the house. . . . I tell you, it was *totally* isolated. And I loved it there !'

To earn the necessary cash for the scanty essentials of life he required while staying there, Tony went to work in a nearby quarry. It sounds an exceeding tough, not to say downright spartan way of life—particularly for a member of the so-called glamorous and sophisticated world of show-business.

But when Tony reminisces about it today, a gradual look of utter wistfulness spreads across his features. Lock the door ! Or it's quite obvious that given half a chance, he'd be back off to the wilds of Northumberland tomorrow.

In fact, he so much prefers burying himself in the countryside, it's somewhat amazing to realise that he was ever located in time in order to make the various film and television appearances he has managed to amass. His films include Peter Brooks' *Meetings With Remarkable Men; The Last Valley* with Michael Caine and Omar Sharif ; Richard Attenborough's *Oh ! What A Lovely War;* and playing Vanessa Redgrave's father in *Isadora.*

For the moment, of course, there is no chance of escaping back to his agricultural roots for Tony Vogel. His current pressure of television toil means the soil has to wait, yet again. He lives, these days, in St. John's Wood, in London. Not that he allows that area to prevent him exercising two hands full of green fingers. He grows some lovely vegetables, by all accounts.

It was the opportunity to portray Dick Barton—the fifth actor only to do so ; and, of course, the very first on television—which tempted Tony to remain a while longer in acting . . . for just a few more very active years, at least.

He has good credentials to be Dick Barton, working his way through various crime-action TV series, from the long forgotten *Department S* and *Paul Temple* to more recent heroics of *The XYY Man, The New Avengers* and *The Return of the Saint.*

Now he leaves them all standing, week after week. All the same, he still lovingly nutures not only his St. John's Wood veg, but his dreams of a farmer's life.

He has, however, many a wicked foe to deal with first.

DANGER FROM THE DEPTHS

'It's happened again!' Snowy exclaimed, looking from the car window as they passed a newspaper seller. Jock Anderson looked back briefly, reading the placard as they sped down the road. . . .

'Sixth ship sunk in London docks.' Jock said quietly. 'What does it mean, Dick?'

'I'm not sure, Jock . . . looks like some sort of huge protection racket. . . .' Dick Barton brought the car gently to a halt at a zebra crossing, smiling briefly at the old woman who shuffled across the road in front of them. 'But how they're doing it, I'm not sure . . . still, I think perhaps it's time we started to find out. . . .'

Snowy White, in the front passenger seat, smiled slightly to himself. 'We need to take the next left turn for the docks. . . .' he said.

A half an hour's drive took them through the shattered remnants of London's East End, still desolate and hardly rebuilt after the wartime bombing. Now the nights were being rent by the sound of explosions once more . . . six ships sunk in the space of ten days. . . .

'The police think they're using some sort of limpet mine . . .' Edwards said, shortly after they had arrived in his office and introduced themselves. 'But how they place them, there's no way of knowing. I had twenty men on watch in my dock last night . . . and eight policemen . . . but they still managed to get through somehow and sink the *Warwick Castle*. . . .'

Edwards was a worried man, Dick could see . . . a very worried man. He sat at the desk with his head in his hands, shoulders slumped. And yet he didn't look the sort of man to let adversity defeat him, broad-shouldered and with a thick black beard. 'I thought everything would be fine when I got out of the Navy . . .' Edwards continued. 'I built up my little fleet . . . nine ships . . . or at least there were nine. Four of them won't be shipping anything but water for a long time. . . .'

'But you're not the only one to lose ships, are you, Mister Edwards?' Snowy asked.

'No . . . Herbert and Thompson have each lost one as well. I've talked to them, and they both agree we shouldn't give in. But what can we do?'

'And they've had demands for protection money as well?'

'Every small shipper in London's had demands!' Edwards said, barely able to control his anger. 'Ten thousand pounds to leave my ships alone! It's impossible, even if I wanted to do it. I only run small cargoes up and down the east coast. I haven't got that much money. . . .'

'And yet you must have lost that much already, surely?' Dick asked.

'More . . . if I lose one more ship, I'm turning it in. Even that'll probably bankrupt me, but it's better to cut my losses . . .'

'We'll do our best to see that you don't have any more losses at all, Mister Edwards,' Dick said, getting to his feet. He, Jock and Snowy walked back to the car. Not far away, they could see the *Warwick Castle* nestled deep in the dock. Only the bridge was above water now. Further along, they could see two other ships in a similar condition. The fourth had been sunk out on the river, and was now lying at the bottom of the Thames.

'It'll cost him a fortune in salvage alone,' Jock remarked. 'Even if it's worthwhile bringing the ships up again.'

'Come on,' Dick said, opening the car door. 'Let's go and have a word with the others . . . Herbert and Thompson. . . .'

But Herbert and Thompson could tell them little more than Edwards. They were both worried men, too, though Herbert was trying to put a brave face on it. The ship he had lost was due for the scrapyard anyway. He'd get by without it. . . .

'Where are we going?' Jock asked, as Dick turned the car east after they left Thompson.

'Along the river . . . I want to check out some of the boathouses. . . .'

'But why?' Snowy asked. 'Obviously they're using frogmen to place the limpet mines . . . we've all guessed that . . . but no frogman would swim all the way down here from the docks. They'd start from somewhere near their target. . . .'

'And the docks are swarming with policemen, sailors and angry ship-owners who want to form vigilante patrols . . .' Dick told him, gunning the engine as they began to leave the suburbs behind.

'No, they have to come along the river from outside . . . probably in a launch. And I'm guessing they come from downriver. Edwards' ship was sunk in the Eastuary. . . .'

'But surely a launch would be seen . . .' Jock put in. 'The last few nights they've been sweeping the Thames with searchlights . . . but the explosions have still been going on. . . .'

'That's the only thing that's worrying me about the idea . . .' Dick admitted. 'Still, it's the best we've got to go on at the moment. . . .'

By mid-afternoon, they had already checked five boathouses, leaving London behind and moving along the Essex coastline. Only two had housed motor-launches. And in both cases the owners had been able to prove they were ashore on the nights of the explosions. Dick was beginning to think this might be a wild goose chase after all. . . .

The road was taking them through open marshland now, the river glistening broadly in the distance to their right. Ahead of them, a trackway led away from the road down to the water's edge, and there was a small, barn-like wooden boathouse. Dick brought the car to a halt at the end of the trackway.

A gate blocked the end of the track, and on it hung a notice boldly proclaiming the area to be private property, trespassers not allowed. Dick hesitated. There was no way of explaining his purpose unless he got closer to the building. He would have to risk the owner's wrath. . . .

Opening the gate, the three of them began striding down the track, eyes fixed on the boathouse, looking for signs of life. A door opened suddenly. An old man appeared, holding a double-barrelled shotgun. Pointing it at the sky, he pulled one of the triggers.

Dick and the others stopped in their tracks as the blast echoed through the still air.

'The next one's aimed at you!' the old man cried, raising the gun to his shoulder. Dick raised a hand placatingly.

'We don't want to trespass . . .' he shouted. 'We only want a few words with the owner!'

'Owner's not here!' the old man snapped. 'Are you going or not?'

'Very soon . . .' Dick assured him. 'But who is the owner?'

'Don't know . . .' the old man said, his patience obviously wearing thin. 'Never see him. He pays me to keep people away from here in the day, and that's what I'm doing. So get out, or I'll shoot . . .'!

Dick took one last look at the man, then turned on his heel. Together, the three of them walked back up to the car.

'What do we do now?' Snowy asked, as they got in.

'We drive down the road a little way . . .' Dick told him. 'Then we find a nice thick hedge to keep us out of sight of the boathouse . . . and wait for nightfall. . . .'

'I thought we'd be going back . . .' Jock said, smiling to himself.

The old man left the boathouse at dusk, and after giving him sufficient time to get clear of the area, Dick, Jock and Snowy moved closer, scanning both the boathouse and the river with binoculars. After half an hour, they heard the whine of an outboard motor, getting swiftly closer. A launch appeared, heading for the boathouse, and disappeared within. Dick nodded to the others, and they moved to within fifty yards of the boathouse. But still they waited. . . .

The time seemed to drag interminably. The moon, nearly full, rose shedding a pale light over the marshland. Then, from the boathouse, came the soft sound of an engine starting up . . . a puzzling, low drone, which Dick knew did not come from a petrol engine. The doors at the front of the boathouse opened, and something emerged into the river.

'A midget submarine!' Dick gasped in spite of himself. Two frogmen, with facemasks, and airtanks on their backs, were riding astride a long, torpedo-shaped craft, its battery-driven electric motors taking it along almost silently. As the midget sub hit deeper water, it submerged, until only the frogmen's heads were visible above the water. They would not submerge completely, and start using their air-tanks, until they were a lot closer to the target. Dick watched them moving away upriver toward the docks, then motioned to Jock and Snowy. Together they moved in towards the boathouse.

The door was locked, but by clambering along the front of the boathouse where it was built out over the river on stilts, they managed to find their way in. The main doors were still open, and the motor-launch lay tied up at one side of the boathouse. At the far end, a row of wooden steps ran up to another door, beyond which Dick guessed would be a couple of small offices. Leaving the others to look round the boathouse itself, Dick headed up the stairs.

Beyond the door was a short corridor, with two doors leading off on either side. The first door revealed a dark, empty storeroom. The second door led into an office. Dick moved forward, switching on the desk lamp. Carefully, he began to search the drawers, pausing when he found a notebook. The top sheet was clean, but Dick could see the impression made when someone had written on the sheet above. That sheet was gone now, but taking a pencil from his pocket, Dick began shading the notebook lightly. Soon the impressions were standing out white against the grey. Dick drew breath sharply. It was a list of sailing times of various ships . . . and they nearly all belonged to Edwards.

'I was hoping I wouldn't see you again, Mister Barton . . .' a calm voice announced suddenly, and Dick looked up to see Thompson, a pistol in his hand. 'You seem to have discovered everything. . . .'

'You mean that the protection racket was just a front . . . and you're really out to ruin Edwards . . .'

Dick Barton turned and there stood Thompson, armed and menacing.

'Exactly . . . my son died on his ship in the war. I've never forgiven him for that . . .'

'But it might not have been his fault,' Dick said quickly. 'It was in the war . . .'

'Even so . . . I must pay him back . . . and I'll go to any lengths to get my revenge. . . .'

'Even to the point of blowing up your own boat to cover your tracks,' Dick said loudly, trying to surprise the man, but Thompson remained calm.

'Even to the point of killing you, Mister Barton . . .' he said, raising the gun. And then, suddenly, he collapsed forward, falling flat on his face. Snowy stood behind him, both fists clenched together, grinning.

'That old double-punch gets them every time,' Snowy said. 'Good job I heard you . . . I guessed it must be trouble. . . .'

'Tie him up, Snowy . . .' Dick said, making a final swift search of the drawers, then shouting to Jock: 'Get that launch untied . . . and start the engine . . . !'

In a matter of moments, Dick and Snowy had joined Jock in the launch, and Dick took the controls, nosing the boat out into the river. The tide was coming in, and the swell assisted the engine in carrying them swiftly upriver.

'Where are we heading?' Snowy asked, as he saw the docks approaching.

'Edwards' shipyard,' Dick told him. 'But keep an eye on the water . . . it's those two frogmen we're after. . . .'

'Shouldn't we try to get ashore to the docks?' Snowy said. 'Warn them . . .'

'Too late for that now, Snowy. According to that list, the *Humber Queen* should have upped anchor by now. They'll probably try to sink her in mid-river . . .'

'There she is now!' Jock said, pointing up river at the coaster that was coming toward them.

'And there are the frogmen!' Dick exclaimed, suddenly seeing two heads protruding from the water, not far away, and turning the wheel toward them. They were still too far away from the coaster to do any harm, so they might have a chance.

But then, to his horror, Dick saw a foaming white trail suddenly lengthening before him.

'Torpedo!' he yelled. 'Over the side, both of you. . . .'

There were two splashes as Jock and Snowy obeyed his orders, and Dick gunned the engine, heading the launch between the torpedo and the *Humber Queen*. It would have to be timed just right. Dick held the wheel for as long as he dared . . . then he too plunged into the dark, cold water. The unladen motorboat roared forward, engine whining.

And then the engine died in a shattering explosion, as the torpedo caught the rear of the launch and blew it out of the water. For a while, there was only light, smoke, noise and flying debris. Almost instantly, spotlights from the shore began sweeping over the river.

The torpedo caught the rear of the launch and a gigantic blast followed.

Looking round, Dick could see Jock and Snowy, treading water like himself, not far away. Dick raised an arm to wave, then saw the two frogmen. They were submerging now, coming toward him. Dick watched them until they disappeared below the water, judging their direction and speed of travel. Then he began waving his arm furiously. One of the spotlights picked him up and held him in its beam.

Waiting a few seconds, Dick filled his lungs, and then plunged beneath the surface. The spotlight above provided just enough light for him to see the midget sub passing by below him, a tubular shadow, a few feet to his side. Dick kicked down toward it.

The leading frogman didn't even see the hand which reached down from above and ripped off his airpipe. A mass of bubbles sped toward the surface, and Dick kicked upwards. Instants later, the frogman came up gasping, saw Dick, and hurled himself through the water toward him. Dick punched him once on the jaw, and then grabbed his neck before the unconscious man could slip back under water.

Still holding up his captive, Dick looked round as there was a splashing nearby. The midget submarine, lightened of one passenger, was coming up of its own accord. As the second frogman emerged into the air, Jock and Snowy were upon him, one from either side.

With his arms under the other man's shoulders, Dick kicked toward the sub, loading his captive back into the forward seat. Under the watchful eye of Snowy, the second frogman began to steer the sub across the surface toward the shore. Dick could already see a reception committee of police and dockers on the shore.

Dick shivered, grinning at Jock and Snowy. It had been a long, hard, wet night . . . and he couldn't wait to get back on dry land again. . . .

HARD ON THE TRAIL OF THE VILLAINOUS VON ROMMITZ, DICK, JOCK AND SNOWY APPROACH THE HOUSES OF PARLIAMENT... WITH ONLY 4 MINUTES AND 50 SECONDS TO GO BEFORE THE FIEND'S BOMB EXPLODES...!

QUICK! JOCK...SNOWY... OVER THE CARS! IT'S THE ONLY WAY!

HOY! MY PAINTWORK...!

CHARGE IT TO DICK BARTON! THIS IS AN EMERGENCY...!

TWO MINUTES DRIFT AWAY BEFORE...

LET US THROUGH, CONSTABLE...IT'S OF THE UTMOST IMPORTANCE...

DICK BARTON! WHAT... OF COURSE, SIR... YOU GO AHEAD...

WHERE DO WE FIND HIM IN A PLACE LIKE THIS? HE COULD BE ANYWHERE!

THE CELLARS ARE MY BET! SNOWY! YOU STAY HERE AND KEEP EVERYONE AWAY...!

AND, AS THE SANDS OF TIME CONTINUE TO RUN OUT...

FASTER, JOCK!

AND THEN, SUDDENLY...

VON ROMMITZ! STAY BACK, JOCK... HE'S ARMED!

CURSES! BARTON! ALWAYS BARTON!

BUT NOW, IN MY MOMENT OF GREATEST TRIUMPH, I SHALL SEE MY BITTEREST FOE DIE TOO!

AND YOURSELF, VON ROMMITZ...YOU'LL NEVER GET OUT IN TIME!

MY LIFE IS NOTHING... COMPARED TO MY ACHIEVEMENT!

WHO IS DICK BARTON?

Richard Barton was born—an Aries, as his sheer dynamism obviously implies—on April 11, 1913, in Norwich. He is the only son of William Barton, then 25, an Ipswich native, and his wife, the former Elizabeth Valerie Clavert, 23, from Muswell Hill, in London. Dick's father was a partner in a large Norwich flour - mill business, which he had first joined as an apprentice.

Dick has—or had; who knows anymore—an uncle, as well. His father's younger brother, Herbert Barton. Uncle Bert. He was last heard of somewhere out East, near Singapore. But he's never actually referred to, at least not by name, in the family anymore. This is presumably due to some darkly secret and typically black - sheep - of - the - family reasons, which continue to intrigue 'and rather amuse' his nephew. For obvious reasons: Dick, after all, would seem to have inherited more of Uncle Bert's daring spirit than of his more averagely genteel, middle-class parents.

Good parents, though; Dick won't hear a word against them. They did him proud. More strong-minded than straight-laced, they were quick to cultivate their lad's inherent flair as a definitive leader of men. This was something he's said to have shown from a remarkably early age — 'when still in rompers,' says his mother—and certainly it's a talent he has never lost. School bullies, for example, soon learned to steer clear of young Barton.

He was educated, in fact, at Norwich School (founded 1250). He went there as a day boy, did well enough in the majority of his studies, and performed quite heroically on the playing fields, excelling in cricket and fives. His best sport was rugby, and he rapidly won his colours in the school's rugger XV.

He left school, hearth and home to take up a civil engineering degree course at Aberdeen University. Graduating with honours in 1934, he joined the Chesterfield drawing office of Tube Investments, Ltd. The job, his first, 'bored the pants off me'. Clearly office life was not for Barton; it stifled his natural instincts and flair for leadership.

Before the year was out, he'd quit Chesterfield to take up a far more adventurous offer— constructing a new harbour in Argentina. He did well; very well. By 1936, he was appointed technical adviser to America's International Engineering Project, Inc. Or: trouble - shooter. A globally roving assignment that suited him perfectly (though he never did find out more about Uncle Bert when he got to Singapore). He stayed in the post for three years, until Hitler interrupted his career.

Dick rushed back to Britain as soon as he was able to escape his American contracts, once World War II was declared. He joined the Royal Engineers in 1939, and after the routine square-bashing and officer training, won his officer's commission just two days after his 27th birthday. A week later he was posted to 212 Field Company, Royal Engineers, with the British Expeditionary Force. He stayed in France until the Dunkirk withdrawals where he won his M.C. (Military Cross) when being wounded while 'fearlessly' laying demolitions during the retreat.

Released from hospital, he transferred to Combined Operations (No. 17 Commando Unit) in August, 1940. Snowy White was his platoon sergeant. Together, they saw active service in the Mid East, South East Asia and European battle zones, with the M.E.F., S.E.A.C. and B.A.O.R. until the end of hostilities.

He had been promoted to Lieutenant in December, 1940, and won his Captain's three pips on February 20, 1945, ten months before joining the ranks of thousands of suddenly demobilised soldiers, caught between returning to old lives, often shattered families and past lives, and striving therefore, for something new in 'a land fit for heroes to live in'.

Many of them preferred to go in for something—anything— that matched the kind of constant danger they had (sadly) become all too accustomed to. Barton, perhaps none too surprisingly, chose this latter course.

The rest is history. . . . The kind of history written in the stars; his stars. Aries happens to be the first sign of the zodiac. Arians tend to put themselves first in most matters. They can't help it. They are known to be fantastic organisers, great leaders, agressively self-willed; naturals for taking charge of any situation or project and unearthing fresh approaches to old formulae. They push themselves to the very limit, usually displaying notable courage and tenacity. And unless they learn how to unwind, they can almost literally burn themselves out.

That's pure Barton.

Fortunately, he can manage to relax. Again in keeping with his sign, he's fashionable in clothes, charming in company— a good listener, a stimulating friend and ally. He suffers the usual Arian faults, as well, though. Quick temper, impatience, impulsiveness, and at times, a possessive jealousy. Selfish in many ways; yet as Dick Barton, friend of the oppressed, proves time and time again, never self-centred.

While it remains a matter of conjecture whether or not fearless Dick Barton could operate without the dependable services of Jock and Snowy, it's obvious that they would be lost without him.

They both served with 'the captain' during the war. They look up to him still, with something close to downright awe. They admire his courage, respect his leadership, and follow his orders—to the hilt. He's an officer and a gentleman of the old school—their hero, their ideal guv'nor. Above all else, he's helped put some colour back into the drab, post-war existence, poured some spirit and adventure into the grey world of ration books, utility clothing, furniture, food—and black-market petrol.

In the first chronicle of their amazing exploits together—on radio—Snowy White was the major cohort of Capt. Barton; Jock arrived later in the series. For television's more lively reconstruction of their finest (quarter) hours, they're together from the outset. As close-knit, as dangerous to tackle as The Three Musketeers. All for one, indeed.

Barton is not one to exactly hide his light under any adjacent bushel. Jock and Snowy, however, are a right pair of dark horses. They don't let on too much about their background, or not unless it proves necessary in the pursuit of criminal factions. They prefer to melt into the shadows and leave the spotlight and the kudos to their guv'nor, 'Capt. Barton, sir.'

So just who—*exactly*—are they, these toughened war-horses? Where do they come from? A swift investigation through the dusty files at the War Office helps supply some of the missing answers. Or as many facts as has ever been itemised about the ubiquitous Messrs. Anderson and White.

One surprise is that Jock is the youngest of the couple; it's merely the traditional taciturn trait of any wiley Scot that makes him, at times, seem Snowy's elder. John Anderson was born in Glasgow on August 13, 1920 and he was still in school fifteen years later when Snowy White was into his second occupation (a driver, of course, for a removal firm: 'good training that,' he laughs, 'for my days driving tanks').

Jock stems from good Scots stock. His father, James Anderson, from Oban, used to be a fisherman until moving into the city and joining the Glasgow police. That's one of the toughest forces in Britain; and Anderson Snr. caught his criminals without a net. Jock's mother, Ann Maclintock of Dundee, worked in a haberdasher's shop before getting married, at 22, on June 3, 1912.

Seven months after those joyous nuptials up in Scotland— George Victor White was born on January 15, 1913, in the self-same house that his father was born in, 12, Windsor Street, Islington. Just next door, in fact, to No. 14, where his mother, the former Maud Briggs, had been born 26 years previously. Until Snowy joined the Army, this branch of the White family didn't exactly travel very far from home. . . .

George Victor, of course, like his father before him, and his before that, like anyone named White in the British Isles, was to become known as Snowy, and long before the hair on his infant's head was much more than peach fuzz.

Snowy's dad, Jack Ernest

swer the call
..... SNOWY !

White, used to be a driver for Carter-Patterson ('he started when their vans were still pulled by horses,' says Snowy); he later switched jobs and became a supervisory loader at a warehouse in Liverpool Road . . . and married the girl next door in 1907.

Young Snowy—a tough little bounder, he was, by all accounts — went to school around the corner at the Clerkenwell Parochial School, in Amwell Street. Not for long. No lad did stay in schooling for long in those days, in that area. By 13, he was into his first job—at Sainsbury's at Islington's Chapel Market. Close enough for him to pop home for (or even with) lunch. Bored with counters, he next followed his father's lead and became a lorry driver for Gower Removals for ten years, until the war gave him some hazardous new routes. In the hot seat of a tank.

Jock Anderson continued his education in Glasgow for the full term in his day—until he was fifteen. He soon won employment in an electronics factory, starting at the very bottom rung on the shop floor, and moving, gradually, into the circuitary drawing-office. A bright lad, Jock, much concerned with furthering himself in life. He took an evening class course in engineering and this enabled

him to leave electronics—'dull stuff', he thought at the time—to join the Rolls Royce plant a Derby in 1937. 'I loved it there' Jock is always happiest when tinkering about with engines However, his apprenticeship was soon enough to be rudely interrupted by the war.

It was Jock who joined the Army first. He was square-bashed into shape and in the engineering regiment, the R.E.M.E., about four months before Snowy, down in London volunteered for service and was posted to the 17/21st Hussars tanks. In 1943 Snowy transferred to No. 17 Commando Unit, where his zeal was recognised promptly. He was made platoon sergeant by a certain Lieut. Richard Barton, M.C.

Dick saw more than enough active service together with Sgt. White in the M.E.F. and S.E.A.C. and they first came across Jock Anderson, when all three were finally stationed in Germany with the B.A.O.R., the British Army on the Rhine. They hit it off straight away. Dick and Snowy talked commandos Dick and Jock talked about engineering; Jock and Snowy just talked — over the odd N.A.A.F.I. pint.

If Jock joined up first, it was Snowy who was first out o khaki, getting his demobilsation papers in January, 1946, one month after, by then, Capt Barton. Jock Anderson remained in service for another four months. Then he, too, was dropped back into civvy street He didn't really know what to do, but rather than returning to Scotland, he settled in London working as a garage mechanic Back with his beloved engines. . . .

Until the day he bumped into Snowy White and Dick Barton and discovered once again that engines aren't everything. A least, not unless they're like people—toned up, revved u with a definite purpose in life

Dick Barton gave Jock an Snowy that purpose. An they've never regretted it. 'No of course ' adds Barton 'have

RULES OF CONDUCT

Five months after BBC Radio launched Dick Barton to an excited audience as 'an experiment —a strip cartoon in sound', the serial was winning the largest audience for any serial, whether on the air, in magazines or the cinema. Hopalong Cassidy and Ken Maynard faded into the sagebrush in comparison to Capt. Barton's adventures. While all children, starved of comic-book heroes and with television still in its post-war infancy, adored Saturday morning movies, they also supplied the largest percentage of the Barton audience. The BBC never had them in mind. 'That is what we've got,' said programme chief Norman Collins, 'and we must act accordingly'.

He immediately wrote a list of five 'signposts' for Dick Barton and his cohorts. The various writers studied his memo and shortly before Barton's first radio birthday, worked out a twelve-point code of conduct, dated August 27, 1947. This was it . . . intriguing reading when compared with the methods employed for most of today's TV heroes.

RULES OF CONDUCT

1. Barton is intelligent as well as hard-hitting. He relies as much upon brains as upon brawn.

2. He only uses force when normal, peaceful means of reaching a legitimate goal have failed.

3. Barton never commits an offence in the criminal code, no matter how desirable the means may be argued to justify the end.

4. In reasonable circumstances, he may deceive but he never lies.

5. Barton's violence is restricted to clean socks on the jaw. The refinements of unarmed combat taught to British Commandos cannot be practised by him or his colleagues. When involved in a brawl which ends in victory for the Barton side, he must be equally matched or outnumbered.

6. Barton's enemies have more latitude in their behaviour but they may not indulge in actually giving any injury or punishment which is basically sadistic.

7. Barton and his friends do not wittingly involve innocent members of the public in situations which would cause them to be distressed. For example, a motor car cannot be requisitioned for the purpose of chasing bandits, without the owner's permission.

8. Barton has now given up drink altogether. No reference should be made to its existence in the Barton circle. The villains may drink but never to excess. Drunken scenes are barred.

9. Sex, in the active sense, plays no part in the Barton adventures. In other words, Dick has no flirtations or affairs and his enemies have no molls or mistresses (as opposed to partners). This provision does not of course rule out the possibility of a decent marriage (not involving Dick personally) taking place.

10. Horrific effects in general must be closely watched. Supernatural or pseudo-supernatural sequences are to be avoided—ghosts, night-prowling, gorillas, vampires.

11. Swearing and bad language generally may not be used by any character. This ban ranges from 'bloody' through 'God', 'Damn' and 'hell' to ugly expressions currently heard in certain conversations but not considered admissable for child usage in middle-class homes.

12. Political themes are unpopular as well as being occasionally embarrassing.The man-who-wants-to-control-the-Earth creates little impact and is best left out of the Barton world.

ANTHONY HEATON
~alias Snowy White

For a Londoner . . . a Yorkshireman. The pride of Islington, Snowy White, is the latest creation of busy Bradford-born actor Anthony Heaton. He was born in 1947 around the time John Mann was immortalising the tough little Londoner on the 'wireless'.

'Obviously, there's quite a bit of myself in the character of Snowy,' says Anthony. 'But one of the best things for me about playing in *Dick Barton, Special Agent,* is reliving a period when I was around . . . although much too young to remember anything about it.'

After training to be an actor at the London Academy of Music and Dramatic Art (LAMDA) in Cromwell Road, the fledgling Heaton career began with a couple of classic murder mysteries in Crewe : *Gaslight* and *Dial M. For Murder.* Next stop : the Marlow Theatre in Canterbury for a full season in repertory. Since when, he has equally divided his talent between the theatre— 'which I prefer'—and television—'which pays better !'

On-stage, Anthony Heaton seems to have played just about everything going. From *Hamlet* (three times : as Fortinbras; the Player King ; and the Gravedigger) to the fiery Petruchio in an Open Space Theatre version of *The Shrew.*

Roaming the country from Stoke to Hornchurch, from Birmingham to Coventry, he's also tackled *The Knack, The Recruiting Officer, Henry V, The Miracle Worker* and Tennessee Williams' *A Streetcar Named Desire.*

He began his television career in Yorkshire in the *Castle Haven* series, and after several plays began taking on the major law and order stars, one by one : *Dixon of Dock Green; Softly, Softly; The Sweeney; The New Avengers* and *Target.* He's also been seen—often—in the much repeated award-winning Jack Gold TV film, *The Naked Civil Servant* with John Hurt.

These days, Anthony Heaton lives in Hampstead with his second wife, the novelist and writer Josie Heaton. (He has a daughter from his first marriage.)

A great love of books is a shared interest with his wife. 'I spend much of my free time reading absolutely anything and everything—*except* science fiction.'

But he's not quite the slouch he makes out. In order to keep fit, as any actor must— especially one joining forces with Dick Barton and Jock Anderson to battle villainy every night of the week—Anthony Heaton plays a lot of squash. And very energetically, at that.

MURDER MANSION

A Scot for a Scot. . . . And thirty-year-old James Cosmo is about as close as you can get to the real Jock Anderson. Both men are Scottish by birth, inherent feeling and sheer style. Both men come from Glasgow. And both have been known to enjoy the occasional spot of river-fishing.

But there, the merely coincidental similarities come to an abrupt end. James Cosmo is no mechanic by nature. He's the actor-son of an actor father: the Scots actor James Copeland. James made his first television appearance close to his home, in the Scots medico series, *Dr. Finlay's Casebook,* with Andrew Cruikshank and Bill Simpson. He didn't wander too far abroad for his next big break, either—*The Borderers.*

'While I'm too young to remember the original radio series of *Dick Barton, Special Agent,*' says James, 'I certainly enjoy the period flavour we manage to maintain in the television series. Great fun to make.

'Although there's a lot of action in the show, it's all totally non-violent. All the fights are good, straight punch-ups, with no nasty tricks. Yes, *great* fun !'

James Cosmo's other television work has proved to be exactly the way actors like it—multi-varied. *Softly, Softly; Sovereigns' Company; The Stone Tapes* and *Wingate*—opposite another dashing TV hero, *Van der Valk*'s Barry Foster. For three series, from 1973, he also played Fuller all at sea in *Warship;* and later became one of *The Survivors.*

His films had him stuck in uniform to begin with—*The Virgin Soldiers,* followed by the star-packed tribute to *The Battle of Britain.* He's also made the big-screen version of TV's *Doomwatch; Assault;* and Sir Richard Attenborough's part-biography of Churchill, *Young Winston.*

Before following in the foot-steps—or is that kilt-steps ?—of Alex McCrindle as Dick Barton's staunch assistant, Jock Anderson, James had completed starring in a new TV series made down-under in New Zealand: *The McKenzie Affair* . . . which sounds rather like yet another instalment of Jock Anderson's hectic life with Dick Barton and Snowy White.

Off duty, James rushes back to Glasgow, where he lives with his wife, Joan, and loves taking the opportunity to retreat into the country-side for his most favoured hobbies. Fishing. Shooting. Hunting. 'Or best of all stalking deer near Inverness.'

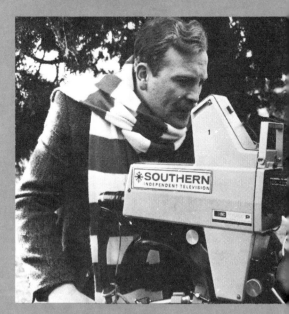

James Cosmo alias Jock A

rson

HELP DICK BARTON FIND THE TIME BOMB

He can still be seen often enough these days on stage, television, movies, and heard as much as ever in radio plays. Thrillers included. The face may be older, though no less handsome, replete still with the indomitable British heroic spirit. His hair is grey. His build stockier, now; more comfortable. He can pass for an aristocratic peer, a judge or some other exalted member of the Establishment.

He only has to deliver a few lines of dialogue, though, and one section of his audience, at home or in the theatre or cinema, will turn to the other and gasp, 'Isn't that . . . ? Yes, by Jove it is . . . ! That's Dick Barton!'

They may not remember his name. They may never have known it. But they can never forget his voice.

His name is Noël Johnson and he was—to some diehards, he still is—Dick Barton for close on four radio years. Until an argument over money. 'Danger money,' is how he phrased his needs. And he required plenty of it, what with having to

handle his collosal fan-mail himself, risking suits every time he simply walked down the street or being mobbed at his more advertised outings for personal appearances. To say nothing of suddenly being faced with a drop in other acting offers.

Full-time employment is a dream for most actors; full-time identification with one role alone often proves a nightmare—at least; fatal at most to a career. Yes, even on radio. Perhaps all the more so on radio, where the audience's identification with stars, factual or fictional, remains rooted in their imagination.

Like the Barton radio serial, Noël Johnson was born in Birmingham; and like Barton himself, Johnson had been wounded at the Dunkirk evacuation. (He was invalided out of the Army in 1941.) He was thirty in 1946, and busily acting with the BBC Repertory Company in various plays and serials and acting as compere for a popular music hour called *Music By* (George) *Melachrino.* One of the producers he often worked with, Martyn Webster, dropped a few hints about a forthcoming daily radio serial. Johnson showed an obvious interest in the anonymous project.

'Would you like to be associated with it?' asked Webster.

'What do you think?' laughed Johnson. 'Work every day!'

And so, even before the serial was in finished script form, or the hero was properly christened, or indeed had found studio space to work in, Noël Johnson was considered definite for the title role. Even by 1946 standards, the money was not brilliant, but the BBC suggested he would be able to make some extra money with personal appearances and other perks—if the serial caught on.

The show, of course, caught on like a brush-fire. Noël Johnson did tour around opening this, closing that. He even starred as a similar kind of hero in a stage show called *Strong and Sweet.* But, according to BBC rules and regulations of the period, he had to refuse an offer from Kelloggs to featured on their Corn Flakes' packs.

Unfortunately, Noël Johnson never made the film versions of his most famous role, either. Don Stannard, unheard of before or since, became the first screened Barton. The movies, however, were no way as thrilling as the radio show was—or the television series is.

When Noël Johnson threw in the towel and quite the special agentry business in 1949, he was succeeded by actor-explorer Duncan Carse, and Gordon Davies wrapped up the radio adventures of Dick, Jock and Snowy.

And now Barton lives again in the firm and capable grasp of Tony Vogel. . . .

PICTURES OF PERIL

'Hardly seemed worth bothering the police with,' Colonel Keene explained. 'It wasn't worth anything, but it's a bit of a mystery why the thief should just take that. That's why I called you . . . know you like a good mystery. . . .'

Dick Barton smiled slightly. Colonel Keene was a good old boy whom he had known for years; but he just didn't understand the often dangerous work that Dick was involved in. Still, he could hardly let down an old friend. . . .

'Just one small watercolour taken?' Dick said. 'And he left all the other paintings behind . . . along with the plate and the money. . . .'

'That's right. . . .' an expression of bewilderment crossed the Colonel's ruddy face. 'Damn strange behaviour for a thief, it seems to me. . . .'

Dick turned to glance toward Jock and Snowy, sitting in armchairs nearby, still fully alert despite the long drive from London. 'There must be something special about that particular picture,' Snowy said.

Dick nodded, turning back to the colonel, who now stroked his walrus moustache thoughtfully. 'Perhaps you'd better tell us more about the painting, Colonel. . . .'

'Didn't have much time to find out anything about it, Dick. Picked it up a couple of days ago at a local auction. There's a group of us . . . Ryan, Wavell, Chambers and myself . . . I think you've met Wavell. . . .' Dick nodded, urging him to continue. 'We form a little group . . . if there's something we like, we buy it between us. Well, there we were . . . Lot 23, I think it was. Four views of the grounds of Canardon House by an unknown artist. They were only about six inches square, and we decided to have them. Got them for a few shillings each . . . just in time. . . .'

'Why was that?' Dick asked, raising a quizzical eyebrow.

'Well, just as we were picking them up from the auctioneer, some young puppy raced into the room . . . in a terrible hurry he was . . . asked what number the auction had reached, and then gave us a terrible glare when he saw us with the watercolours. Next thing on the list was a much larger picture of Canardon House itself, by the same chappie. And this young puppy bid ten pounds for it, straight off. Knocked the wind out of everybody's sails. I mean, something like that takes all the fun out of it . . . the cut and thrust of bidding against one another. . . .'

'I see . . . and this young man . . . what did he do then?'

'Don't really know. He paid up for the picture I suppose . . . but the next time I looked round he'd gone. . . .'

Getting to his feet, Dick began to pace the large Victorian drawing room slowly, deep in thought. 'Can you describe this young man for me, Colonel? He might be more important than you think. . . .'

'Not much to describe, really . . . thin, lanky, slouched around . . . wouldn't have been able to do that in my regiment! Sports jacket, dark trousers, fair hair . . . that's about all I can remember. . . .'

'It's enough to start on, Colonel. You're not on the telephone are you?'

'No, can't stand the new-fangled things . . . always waking you up at night . . . had enough of them in the war, my boy. . . . Still, the other three are. . . .'

'Very well, Colonel, we'll see what we can find out. Firstly, perhaps, you could give us the addresses of Ryan, Wavell and Chambers. . . .' As the colonel began hunting for a pen, Dick turned back to his companions. 'I'll run you back into town . . . from there you should be able to pick up cabs. . . . Snowy, you visit Wavell, Jock Chambers . . . and I'll take Ryan. Tell them what's happened and ask them to let you bring their pictures . . . we'll meet at Ryan's and take a look at all three. . . .'

'And we'll phone you if anything's amiss . . .' Jock added.

Dick nodded, then turned to receive the addresses from the Colonel. 'Something to get your teeth into, eh, my boy?' Keene grinned. 'I almost wish I was coming with you. Not much for an old soldier to do these days, is there?'

Dick suppressed a smile. As an ex-soldier, he found plenty to do. . . .

*   *   *

Giving his hat to the butler, a formal old man who betrayed no emotion at the name Barton, Dick walked into the study. Ryan's house was very much like Keene's . . . a large Victorian house in fairly small grounds, a few miles from town. But as he explained his reasons for calling, Dick quickly saw that Ryan, though also in his sixties, came from a completely different background to Colonel Keene. Ryan had all the appearances of an academic . . . a long-serving college don who had now retired to the country to write. There was an untidy pile of manuscript pages scattered over the desk.

'The watercolour of Canardon, Mister Barton?' Ryan said. 'Yes, I think it's around here somewhere . . . hold on a moment. . . .' Ryan scratched his balding head, then loped swiftly across the room to the bell-pull. A few moments later, the butler appeared at the door.

'Ah, Johnson . . . that little watercolour I brought home the other day. . . . Blowed if I can remember where I put it. . . .'

'It's in the dining room alcove, Sir,' Johnson replied patiently.

'Fetch it in here then, would you, old chap?' Ryan turned back to Dick as Johnson withdrew silently. 'Wonderful fellow . . . don't know what I'd do without him. . . .'

The phone rang suddenly.

'I think that may be for me,' Dick announced, striding toward the desk before Ryan could ring for Johnson to answer it. He picked up the receiver, and as he listened, his expression became serious.

'I'm afraid I've got some rather bad news, Mister Ryan,' Dick said when he finally put down the phone. 'You're friend Wavell is in hospital. Seems he surprised a burglar last night . . . there was a struggle and Wavell got the worst of it. He's still unconscious . . . and his picture's gone as well. . . . This is all getting a little more serious than I thought. . . .'

Ryan threw himself into an armchair, obviously shocked. At that moment, Johnson knocked and entered . . . and Dick was relieved to see that he held the painting in one hand.

'Some tea, I think, Johnson,' Ryan put in quickly . . .'to calm my nerves. Will you join me, Mister Barton?'

'Thank you,' Dick said, moving quickly to take the picture from Johnson before he left the room again. The phone rang once more before he had time to study the watercolour. A rich Scottish accent announced the caller as Jock Anderson.

'Chambers' picture is gone as well?' Dick exclaimed, surprised.

'Aye . . . he didn't know anything about it . . . when we went to check on it, it was gone . . . and nothing else stolen either. . . .'

'All right, Jock . . . here's what I want you to do. Go back into town to the auction room, and see if you can find out the name and address of the man who bought the large picture . . . lot 24. Then join me here at Ryan's. . . .'

Ryan had by now lapsed into silence, still stunned by the news of his friend. As Johnson appeared with the tea, Dick settled back in a chair by the desk to study the watercolour. There seemed to be very little special about it . . . simply a view of the small lake at Canardon: a swan on the water, a bench on the shore, a few trees. And Ryan assured him that the other three pictures had shown little more spectacular than this. Shortly afterwards, Snowy arrived, and Dick filled him in on what had happened.

'Wavell's picture wasn't anything special,

apparently,' Snowy said. 'His wife tells me it was just a view of the maze at Canardon. Mainly the opening in the hedge where you go in, with a couple of large posts on either side. . . .'

'That's odd,' Dick said thoughtfully. 'I know the maze at Canardon. There aren't any posts by the entrance. . . .'

Snowy shrugged. 'But what's so special about Canardon House anyway? It's a hundred miles from here . . . at least. . . .'

'Lord Ritchie's place . . . the only thing special about it is that it was robbed a few years ago. Ritchie's accountant did it. They caught him, and for all I know he's still in jail for it . . . but they never found the loot . . . it was all gold, too. . . .'

'How much was it?'

'Priceless . . . even melted down, the gold alone was worth a hundred thousand pounds. As objets d'art . . . name your own price. . . .'

Snowy whistled softly in surprise. 'Then you think these pictures might have something to do with that?'

'Who knows . . . it was a long time ago . . . before the war. . . .'

An hour passed before Jock arrived at the house, with both good and bad news.

'I found the laddy who bought the other picture. But he's just a local boy . . . apparently a stranger came up to him, gave him twenty pounds, and told him to go in and buy the pictures . . . any change left he could keep. He's kicking himself now for having bid so much. The other man wasn't particularly pleased about missing the earlier pictures either. . . .'

'But he had no idea who the man was?'

'Never seen him before . . . or since. I'm afraid that's a dead end. . . .' All he could remember was that it was a fairly young man, with a hat and long coat . . . he was more interested in the money than who gave it to him.'

Barton turned the picture over thoughtfully, but there seemed nothing on either the back or the frame to give any clue. Finally, he turned back to Ryan.

'I wonder if you'd permit us to stay here tonight, Mister Ryan? I think you may be getting an unwanted caller. . . .'

*　　　*　　　*

It was past midnight, and the darkness was total in Ryan's dining room. At various points round the room, Dick, Jock and Snowy waited, perfectly still, listening to the sound of each other's breathing. If the burglar was coming, it would probably be soon now. . . .

From the corner of his eye, Dick caught a faint flash of light from beneath the door. Then, very soft, the sound of a footstep. All of them tensed as they heard the door handle turn slowly. . . .

Then the door was opened, and a beam of torchlight stabbed through the darkness. It roved over the walls until the watercolour was caught in the light. Then the dark figure of a man began striding purposefully toward it.

The door opened and a beam of torchlight stabbed through the darkness.

At that moment, Snowy snapped on the electric light, slamming the door shut. Dick and Jock sprang from cover to confront the young man . . . and he panicked, making a desperate grab for the picture on the wall. Jock was on him immediately, grabbing his arms and pinning them to his sides.

'Now then, laddy . . .' Jock began. 'Who are you?'

The man stared sullenly at the floor, saying nothing.

'I think we know that already,' Dick cut in. 'Don't we, Mister Mackenzie. . . .'

From the man's startled expression, Dick knew that he was right. 'Son of that other Mackenzie . . . the one who robbed Canardon House. And I suppose these pictures contain some clue to where the gold is, right?'

'Think what you like!' Mackenzie said briefly.

The door to the dining room opened, and Ryan entered, wearing a long dressing gown.

'You've got him then?' the old man said, moving forward to take a close look at Mackenzie. And in that moment of distraction, the burglar managed to twist free of Jock's grasp. With a desperate howl he flung himself toward Ryan, knocking him aside . . . and then he was out of the door before anyone could stop him.

Dick was after him in a flash, with Jock and Snowy close behind. But Mackenzie was out of the house before they could reach him, racing away down the driveway. In the distance, Dick could see a car waiting by the gate.

Mackenzie was young and fast, but he had none of the perfectly trained fitness of Dick and his friends. By the time they approached the end of the drive, Dick was catching up fast. A final sprint, a flying leap . . . and Dick brought his man down with a perfect rugby tackle.

Mackenzie hit the driveway hard, breath bursting from his lungs, and then lay there as Jock and Snowy caught up, all the fight knocked out of him.

Dick made his way to the empty car as Snowy removed Mackenzie's trouser belt and lashed his hands firmly together with it. The other three pictures were in the boot, wrapped in newspaper. Dick switched on the car's headlights and laid the pictures out on the ground, staring at them thoughtfully.

'You're a fool, Mackenzie,' Dick said, looking toward the prisoner, now sitting on the ground between Jock and Snowy. 'You didn't have to steal the pictures . . . a look would have been enough. . . .'

'They should be mine by right!' Mackenzie said bitterly. 'My father painted them in jail, before he died. They should have come to me . . . not been sold for charity. . . .'

'There were other ways. . . .' Dick said. 'You could have just visited the owners and looked at the paintings . . . now you've lost everything. . . .'

'Lost?' Mackenzie laughed, some bravado coming back into his voice. 'No . . . only delayed. What'll I get? A year? Two years, for beating up the old man. . . .'

'By which time it'll be far too late,' Dick cut in coldly. 'Because I know what the pictures mean now. . . .'

All three of them looked at him in surprise as Dick picked up the pictures and went over to them. 'It was this picture of the maze that gave me the clue . . . there aren't any posts there . . . so they're not posts. They're "Ones" . . . and on Ryan's picture . . . the swan is like a figure "2" . . . the end of the bench is drawn to represent a "4". Each picture has two numbers on it. . . . Eight in all. . . .'

Jock and Snowy still stared at Dick uncertainly, but Mackenzie's head had already dropped. He knew the game was up.

"Eight numbers . . .' Dick continued. 'I'm betting they're the numbers of a deposit box . . . probably in a Swiss bank. And that's where the gold from Canardon House is kept. By the time you get out of jail, Mackenzie, that gold will have been back with its rightful owners for quite a long time. . . .'

Dick smiled to himself. What had seemed like a simple wild goose chase had enabled him to crack one of the most important unsolved crimes in the books. 'Take him back to the house, Snowy. . . .' He said. 'The local bobbies can pick him up now. . . .'

Dick Barton, Cinema Agent. Don Stannard played radio's hero in three films between 1948-50. Dick Barton At Bay was the last, in which our hero freed a British scientist held prisoner by foreign agents in the Beachy Head lighthouse. First, he had to free himself, Tamara Desni as Anna and George Ford as the faithful Snowey.

From left to right:
Gordon Davies
Duncan Carse
Noël Johnson

Tony Vogel

FOUR
FACES
OF
DICK
BARTON